STARTING OUT OR STARTING OVER

Top 10 Tips for Runners: Advice, Injuries, & Support.

Plus! Bonus Habit Shaper and Willpower Builder

KATE CHAMPION

STARTING OUT OR STARTING OVER
Top 10 Tips for Runners: Advice, Injuries, & Support.
Plus! Bonus Habit Shaper and Willpower Builder

Published by Mountain Morning Press, Ltd.
ISBN: 978-1-7344806-2-7 (paperback)
ISBN: 978-1-7344806-3-4 (ePub)
Also available for Kindle

Design, layout, and pre-press: Lighthouse24
Cover graphic: Lisa Kolbasa

Publisher's Legal Disclaimer

This book presents a wide range of opinions about a variety of topics related to physical health, mental health, diet, exercise, and general well-being including certain ideas, treatments, and procedures that may be hazardous without proper medical advice. The material presented is not intended as medical and/or healthcare advice. Please consult your healthcare provider before starting any supplements, diet, and/or exercise program. The author, the publisher, and any participants disclaim responsibility for any adverse effects directly or indirectly from any information contained in this book.

*To all those
with the courage
to start out or start over...*

Contents

"The willingness to show-up changes us.
It makes us a little braver each time"
– *Brene Brown*

Introduction

THE IDEA FOR THIS BOOK literally came to me in the middle of the night. That creative part of my brain insisted that I get up and make some damn notes. In that sleepy fog, I saw myself crafting this little book along with its siblings – of course, it's a series! I imagined them like little messengers, offering valuable information, support, and encouragement, serendipitously falling into the hands of people who need them. Written from the heart, with efficiency in mind, this book is short and to the point. No BS. No artificially generated content. No gimmicks. No tricks. I hope you'll find it helpful.

It's a familiar story, I have spent the last twenty-five years of my life raising a family, running a home, building a career – I am a mental health professional; now in private practice. I have chased horses, taken care of dogs, run more errands than humanly possible, cooked enough meals to circle around the sun and back, driven a zillion miles, sat in countless life-sucking meetings gazing out of the window wishing I was out on the trail somewhere – all in the spirit of loyalty, love, and commitment. Let me be clear: I am not complaining – well, maybe a little bit, especially the part about having to sit in all those life-sucking meetings. I chose those paths and wouldn't change them for the world.

Curiously, I find myself in an interesting place. Probably due to two factors: my children have blossomed into self-sufficient, well-adjusted adults, out in the world doing their own version of life. And, after much deliberation I resigned from my big girl job after fifteen years of service. With the job gone and kids out of the house it feels like I can see space on my proverbial plate again.

For some people this is scary. For others, it's a sweet spot where we get another opportunity to start something new or start something over; to decide how we want to fill our plates based on our values, our interests, and who we are at this point in our lives. When I reflect on my "What's next?" the answer is pretty clear: grow my private practice, write, and spend as much time as possible outside exploring nature – mostly on foot – running, hiking, backpacking.

Athletically, I consider myself a late bloomer. Although I started road running – that sounds way grander than any of my actual effort – in my teens; I discovered trail running in my late forties. Seemingly overnight, the trail, and all things green, and piney, and muddy, and far away from civilization became my happy place. I started backpacking in my mid-50s, which – as an aside – also provided the inspiration for my first book *Never Too Late: Inspiration, Motivation, and Sage Advice from 7 Later-in-Life Athletes.*

By all accounts, I aim to squeeze another thirty years or so out of this life, which is good because my brain continues to send up lots of 'ideas' for the next project or adventure. Frankly, it feels like I have more 'book' concepts and 'bucket list' ideas on my to-do list than lifetime left to accomplish them.

A long time ago I heard a someone describe life in a way that still strikes me. I quote:

> "Life is not a journey to the grave with the intention of arriving safely in a pretty and well-preserved body, but rather to skid in broadside, thoroughly used up, totally worn out, and loudly proclaiming – WOW! What a Ride!" – Anonymous.

At its core, this book – regardless of age or ability – is all about advocating, supporting, and inspiring people to start out or dust off a path which may have been misplaced during the messy skirmishes of life.

What can you expect to learn in the following pages? Well, you'll find an extension of my experiences as a later-in-life athlete sprinkled with my background as a counselor, and advocate, who helps people build habits and sustainable life-styles. More importantly, you will also encounter wisdom – sage advice – from your peers, other back-of-the-packers, in all ages, stages, and phases of life.

Written in sections, you can read traditionally, from cover to cover, or you can skip around using information as you need it. Personally, and professionally, I enjoy working with people who are learning something new or starting over. Be it a habit, a behavior, or a skill – Section One is all about starting out or starting over.

A funny thing about starting out, and starting over, is that we forget that we are naturally experts in both these areas. Think about all the times you have started something from nothing or had to begin again. That starting energy – if framed in a helpful way – can be harnessed and used as a superpower – more on that later.

This line of thinking leads us naturally to Section Two where we learn about how habits are built and maintained, and the role that willpower plays in the process. This section presents some fresh concepts about habit building. By the time you finish reading and working through the questions in this section you will have a better understanding about the what, why, and how of your personal habit-building process. In Section Two you'll create your own habit-building map, along with an action plan that enhances the potential within your window of tolerance. If this sounds puzzling – no worries; these are new concepts. I will guide you through this section using real life examples, helpful hints, and tips. If you're serious about creating a sustainable running habit or dusting off that running habit you used to have, then this is the place for you!

Then we jump into the Top 10 Tips with Sage Advice – Section Three. Pretty simple really. No smoke and mirrors here, just authentic tips, sage advice, and inspiration from people in the running community. Folks who have been there and done that. It's the community aspect that makes this my favorite section. No artificial intelligence or computer-generated data just down to earth information straight from your peers directly to you.

Let's face it, if you move, you are likely to get injured. Recently, I went through a six-month cycle of recovering from various injuries. I had my first ever broken bone resulting in surgery in my mid-fifties, three weeks before my bucket list Grand Canyon rim-to-rim hike was scheduled. So frustrating. Then, while running, I tripped over thin air and smashed both knees on the concrete. Then flu season arrived and I was hit hard by a bout of the flu. After the annoyance cleared, I could remind myself that I have run, hiked, and backpacked thousands and thousands of miles over my lifetime with nothing more than an irritating tweak or ache here and there.

Consequently, Section Four is all about injury prevention. Yes, running is a great form of exercise. And, yes, injuries are a thing. According to one study, the beginner runner is twice as likely to report an injury compared to a more advanced runner. Moreover, there is nothing more frustrating than working hard on building that running habit only to get benched by an injury. This section presents information about the top five most prevalent running related injuries. You'll learn about possible causes, what you should be looking for, and what to do if a pesky injury comes your way.

Next is the Bonus Section: Habit Shaper and Willpower Builder. Did you know we have limited supplies of willpower? Or that willpower can be trained and built like a muscle? We'll start with shaping habits, then move into building willpower. Using a worksheet format, this section will help you to get crystal clear about your goals, your whys, and your action plan. The twist here is that you'll also be making a plan for the rough days. Those days – and, believe me, we all have them – when you'll feel too tired, too hot, too whatever to run.

You will also learn about how willpower ebbs and flows. You'll be invited to make an action plan for times when your reserves of willpower are low. Imagine. Wouldn't having some tools to push through those low willpower times be awesome? Plus, here's the kicker – every time you do push through those slumps your brain lights-up with powerful chemicals that create positive feelings, which in turn make it more likely that you will repeat the process! Furthermore, at the time of writing, I do not believe there is another book covering this information – with access to accompanying worksheets – on the market. It is my hope that the concepts outlined within these pages will add a fresh perspective to the great information we already have. A new rung as people work their way up the habit-building ladder.

In closing, I acknowledge the running community and all the people who made this book possible. You'll find some final words and ways to connect with more support – helpful for people starting out and starting over. Many of the resources that have been helpful in my journey or the journeys of other back-of-the-packers I have met along the way can be downloaded at: https://katechampionauthor.com/resources/.

Dedicated to you and the running community, my hope is that this little book will become a companion; something helpful that's got your back – time and time again if needed. Because, the truth is, we all need a helping hand now and again. Ready to jump in?

SECTION I

Starting Something New

Starting Something New

"...and suddenly you just know it's time to start something new and trust the magic of the beginning."

– unknown

LET ME ACKNOWLEDGE ONE THING – loud and clear – starting something new is not easy. If starting something new and then sustaining it were simple, we would all be rushing around proudly announcing to the world that our goals, hopes, and dreams are 100% accomplished, 100% of the time – thank-you very much. Easy as pie. No worries. Folks, the reality is that starting something new is not as easy as it sounds.

As humans we are wonderfully complex, yet, also full of annoying contradictions. Contradictions and complexities that arise in the different internal voices that – at least in my head – appear to be in constant debate. Even after ten years of consistent running my brain still throws me with a line from one of my classic internal conflicts.

To illustrate, here's a play by play from inside my head. Every morning I make a focus list for the day. Nothing grand; simply a Post-it note with my priorities for the day. One of the tasks I have clearly marked is 'run' or 'workout'. For this item I add a specific time – generally 4 to 5 pm. At about twoish I glance over my small, totally doable list. Recall, I am a mental health clinician with a gazillion years of education and practice under my belt. I am trained to help people figure this stuff out. I have also worked hard to understand what works for me and my particular persnickety personality.

Another hour and three-thirty ticks around. Then. Without any conscious thought on the horizon. There's a tiny whisper way in the back of my brain that says, "Dude, it's cold outside. You're tired. You're hungry. Plus, it's getting late." This, "it's getting late" business always cracks me up – I am the one who made the schedule based on my preferences! It's times like this when I seriously begin to question – "Who the heck is in the driver's seat anyway?" I share this not to scare you, but to validate that this is totally normal. There's even a term for it – *stinkin' thinkin'*.

Stinkin' Thinkin'

The term stinking thinking originated in the 1950s with American psychologist Albert Ellis' concept of 'good thoughts' and 'bad thoughts'. Over time, Ellis' theories became the foundation for many of the cognitive based psychotherapy models we use today. In recent years the phrase stinking thinking has evolved into stinkin' thinkin'; popularized by twelve-step recovery communities as a way to call out problematic thoughts that have the potential to lead a person to unhelpful choices or behaviors.

Fast forward to today. We are still a long way from figuring out the deeper intricacies of the brain and how the heck our thoughts work. That said, thanks to science and research in the fields of psychology, cognitive science, and neuroscience we are beginning to have a better understanding about human thought processes. We now know that thoughts – the good, the bad, and the ugly – are, in reality, little more than bursts of energy that arise over and over in the brain. Our thoughts are shaped by our conditioning.

If you are starting out or starting over, these are important concepts. Consider for a moment if thoughts are literally just little bursts of energy with no strings attached, then no judgement is needed. This is big. Please etch this into your brain – *no judgement is needed.*

Thoughts Aren't Facts

Here's another kicker. Science also tells us that thoughts are not facts. Again, news flash – *thoughts are not facts.* Just because we have a thought doesn't mean it's an absolute command to act. Yes, a thought is probably a signal for something – but a hard, take it to the jury fact; not so much.

This, my fellow running friend, is a gift because it allows you, the thinker, a moment to pause. To question that thought. To examine. To inquire, "Is this thought helpful?" To be curious, "Hmm, I wonder what this thought is about?"

Why does this matter? It matters because it means that we can learn to stop listening to all that ridiculous back-chatter. All those old crusty worn-out tapes that drone on and on. All those pesky whispers whining about being "too cold, too hot, too late, too tired" can respectfully go on the backburner, be asked to "hush up", and go away.

I acknowledge that the science behind this is complicated, way above my pay grade, and far beyond the scope of this book. However, with the use of a personal scenario here's my humble attempt to simplify how this thought stuff works.

Here we go...

I'm driving my car through the automatic carwash. I find myself intrigued by the rainbow-colored soap concoction – there's sight, sound, and fragrance as the frothy foamy liquid starts oozing down the windows. The brushes kick-on whirling in unison with cascades of water. Then those black flappy things spring to life as they start to work their magic. Then I notice the thoughts, "Hmm, I wonder if they use hot or cold water? I could roll down the window just a bit and see..." Seriously! Who thinks that?

Anyway, back to my point. "I could roll down the window" is without a doubt a thought – and, yes, in reality, it is also a fact. I could literally roll down the window and stick my hand out and test the temperature of the water. Thankfully, my brain also has a frontal cortex which allows for a smidge of impulse control and the proclivity for self-reflection. These abilities are like the guardrails on a twisty mountain road. They protect me from going over the edge. Together, impulse control and self-reflection work as a team, helping me realize that this thought is neither a *fact* nor something I *must* do – it's simply good old-fashioned curiosity. Having the thought, "I wonder..." simply led to a feeling: curiosity. By nature, I am a pretty curious person. In a flash the world makes sense and I can finish the carwash – without getting soaked.

Remember, earlier I said we are complex creatures? Our internal workings include a rich blend of thoughts, feelings, emotions, values, and beliefs. Whether you are aware of it or not; you too have a similar array of mental gymnastics going on in your head. Yes, your themes may be different from my themes – but trust me, they're there; alive and well. And, if left untended your thoughts are likely running your show. Not so helpful when we are trying to build a habit or start something new.

Starting Energy

Like everything in life there are two sides to this particular coin. The helpful side, when used in a skillful way, is known as starting energy. Starting energy is a wonderful force. In my case starting energy is a blend of feelings: excitement, pride, accomplishment. Accompanied by loud, "I frickin' love this..." thoughts streaming through my head.

The unhelpful side of starting energy is the freeze response. Yep, I've experienced this too... In my world when this happens, a total brain fog sets in. There I am – stuck, like a stick sinking in quicksand. On this side of the coin the energy is heavy, hopeless, despondent with loud, "What were you thinking; you're no good at..." type of thoughts.

Missing Link #1

The Window of Tolerance is a clinical concept originally developed to help people with trauma and early childhood attachment disruptions understand and manage their body/brain reactions. The notion that we all have thoughts and feelings that ebb and flow depending on what our social/emotional systems are detecting, think window of tolerance – is also deeply rooted in the science behind Porges' Polyvagal Theory. Together, these concepts – stinking thinking and window of tolerance – have been invaluable in informing the way we approach and treat traumatic stress. Curiously, these approaches have been slow to produce tools designed to help the general population manage everyday work/life stress – including the challenges involved in the habit building process.

Okay, I can see your eyes glazing over... enough with the clinical stuff already, "How does this help me?" Great question! It's helpful because these concepts are universally human – we *all* have a polyvagal nerve and we *all* have our unique, personal window of tolerance. I believe that we can adapt the learnings from science and clinical practice and apply them to our everyday lives.

A better grasp on our own personal window of tolerance, in my opinion, is often a missing link when we are trying to create a new habit – like running. Once we can see that our internal responses – helpful or unhelpful – are simply the system's way of interpreting something then we can learn to be more effective at steering the vehicle – body/brain – in the direction we *choose* rather than feeling like we are driving around on automatic pilot.

Additionally, if we can develop a clear picture of our own range of responses – thoughts, feeling, etc. – and if, when starting or restarting a habit, we can keep those responses within a comfortable range (window), then we are more likely to feel happier, healthier, more flexible – which, importantly, increases the likelihood that we will repeat the behavior we are trying to habitualize.

Again, this is in no way intended to be clinical advice or replace well qualified professional help. I am simply taking some threads – science, clinical background, performance enhancement, and personal experience – and offering another, hopefully, more sustainable way for people to get started and stay moving.

SECTION II

Building a Sustainable Habit

Building a Sustainable Habit

"Incredible change happens in your life
when you decide to take control of what you
do have power over instead of craving
control over what you don't..."

— *Steve Maraboli*

AN AMAZING AMOUNT HAS BEEN WRITTEN about motivation and
habit building. A quick Google search for the term 'habit building'
returned more than 233,000,000 results. Although I have read my
fair share of studies, books, articles, and blogs it would take
several lifetimes to read and digest all the information available.
Plus, what we know about habit and willpower is constantly
evolving.

One thing I do see as a gap in the mainstream habit building
literature is that there is little discussion about how our primary
emotions are related to autonomic functioning and how our
physiological state reacts to our environment. Put another way, we
are the Ferrari of the species – incredibly engineered, extremely
complex – with the capacity for remarkable performance. Yet, each
year approximately 45% of Americans make at least one New
Year's resolution. What are the three most popular resolutions? To
lose weight. To start exercising. To stop smoking. At the six-month
mark guess how many people are still on track with their New Year
goals? Less than 50%.

If we are so complex, capable, and proficient why is it so
hard to create and sustain a new behavior – or habit? I think

there's another missing link that may be a connection between our primary emotions, our autonomic functions, and our physiological states.

Missing Link #2

The truth is we are *not* one-size fits all creatures. What works for Sally probably won't work for Pedro. In my humble opinion, global messaging about *"How to Form a New Habit (In 8 easy steps)"* or *"18 Tricks to Make New Habits Stick"* – the two top Google search results at the time of writing – stand on shaky ground. Sure, they offer good information, but they are missing some key foundational elements: the emotions, autonomic functions, and our physiological states (how we are feeling) – all of which are constantly changing. It's these components, in my opinion, that help us better explain why Sally can comfortably build a habit after about thirty days and why Pedro is still struggling at the sixty-day mark.

I contend that if we can understand our own windows of tolerance and overlap that knowledge with our unique abilities and strengths, we can build our own personal bridges. Bridges that connect both – big picture science with unique individual needs – to increase our chances of creating and building that running/walking habit.

Window of Tolerance

Acknowledging that, in many disciplines, there is often a big gap between academia and the real world, one of my intentions, both in my graduate work and professional life, is to try and make complex concepts more digestible. So here goes...

Let's start with the Window of Tolerance. Here are a couple of things you need to know:

- Everybody has one – yes, even you!
- Our windows – like fingerprints – are similar, yet unique.
- Our personal zones of optimal functionality lie within our windows.
- The goal is to understand your window and use it to build your running habit.

What does all this mean? Let's break it down. Like I said, "Everybody has a window" and when you are inside your window of tolerance – also think 'in your comfort zone' your polyvagal nerve – a bundle of nerves that, like ticker tape in New York City's Times Square, is constantly running messages back and forth between the brain and the body, scanning both the internal system and the external environment for safety and danger.

Basically, if you are breathing, the eternal question all our bodies are running around with (pardon the pun), are "Am I safe?" and/or "Am I in danger?" Plus, we all have unique ranges of what we personally can, and can't, tolerate.

Imagine, for a moment, that we are flies on the wall in a room where we put ten random people with the same stressor – let's say a decent sized spider (a particular favorite of mine) – we would likely see a range of stress responses. Let's see...

- Person A might scream, hide her face in her hands, and want to run away.
- Person B could simply be curious; just keeping an eye on the spider.
- Person C may whip off her shoe in an attempt to squish it.
- Person D might move to stop person C from squishing the spider and suggest other options.
- Person E may have a massive stress response and faint.

I could go on. The point I am making here is that we are all doing a version of this dance, all the time, including when we are trying to start a new habit/behavior.

To see this in action take a look around. Reflect on your friends, family, co-workers, neighbors. Imagine it's New Year's Eve. Maybe you see people in your circle who want to 'get healthy'? Even the concept of 'getting healthy' has a range of responses. Jane might want to start running. Jim might decide to dust off his bike. Andrea signs up for a yoga class. And Juan commits to cutting out meat and dairy products. All great – and very different – ways of 'getting healthy'.

If you look a bit closer you will also notice that some of these folks will stay within their range of tolerance and, fairly comfortably, create the sustainable behavior change they are seeking. For other people, this experience will be uncomfortable creating a variety of mental and/or physical distress. The group of distressed people are probably outside their respective windows of tolerance – the kiss of death for creating a sustainable behavior change. Why? Because discomfort creates a barrier, blocking progress and quickly sabotaging all those good intentions. Additionally, feelings like 'frustration' and 'disappointment' and thoughts like "Geez, what the heck is wrong with me? Why can't I get this...?" jump into the mix creating more unhelpful internal energy which compounds the problem – providing even more evidence that you should plonk your rear end right back down on that couch. I get it. I've been there too.

One of the complaints I hear about the array of *How to Build Habits* books published in the last five years or so is that "There's nothing new. Yes, the foundational information we have about habit building – cue, routine, reward – is super helpful, however, where are the new perspectives?" – an inquiry made by one reviewer. As noted previously, I have consumed a fraction of the mountain of literature out there about changing behaviors and habit building. Still, it is my hope that these pages will add a new twist to the knowledge we already have.

Changing Behavior and Building Habits

Here goes – let me see if I can communicate this in a way that makes sense. I'll start with 'the window'. As mentioned previously, we are all wired with our unique zones of comfort and zones of discomfort. When we are navigating our daily tasks within our zone (window) of comfort our internal systems (the body) feels open, trusting, and safe – allowing feelings to emerge such as curiosity, humor, and determination. Such feelings encourage our brains to access helpful cognitive processes like the ability to plan, reason, and think clearly – all vital components in creating habits. When we are within our window of tolerance, we feel good – like we have a grasp on life. When our systems are regulated, we feel calm. Our mind feels solid. Like a well-oiled machine – all our parts are working smoothly, in harmony.

Then, when life throws us that inevitable curve ball, we begin to shift outside our window of tolerance. As this happens our systems begin to move in one of two directions.

Direction A: If you can imagine, space *above* the window. This – above the window space – will create feelings such as overwhelm, anxiety, and frustration. When we are above our window our brains are not thinking clearly – I call this scrambled egg brain. Our breath is shallow, we may notice heat in the body, or tightness in the chest. At some point, we may be filled with "Screw this! I hate running" energy or anxious "I'm never going to be any good at this" thoughts – either way we find ourselves throwing our shoes back into the closet. You can probably imagine – above the window energy is not helpful for building that running, or any other, habit for that matter.

Direction B: If you can imagine, space *below* the window. When we are here it's all about shutting down. We might feel spacy, disconnected, or what I call, deer in the headlights energy. We may freeze or feel numb. Here the thoughts might be, "Why bother?" "What's the point?" The energy is blah – like you want to crawl back into bed and pull the covers over your head. **Helpful Hint:** There is no 'right' or 'wrong' direction here; again, much of this will depend on how we are wired (and early childhood stuff). Regardless, either direction will take us, to varying degrees, outside our comfort zone. It's that sense of taking two steps forward and then three steps back which again, in the early stages of habit building, is not helpful.

I recognize that this a lot of information. Here is a visual representation with examples of some of the corresponding feelings that are likely to arise.

Above and Below the Window

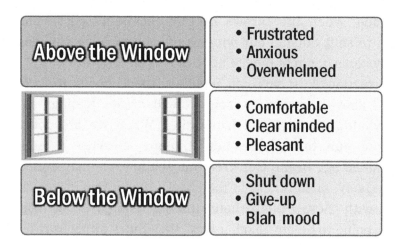

Now you have a better idea about the concept. Here are a few points I want you to remember:

- Just like a house, we have lots of windows.
- Our windows can be wide or narrow.
- We have different windows for different situations.
- We have high tolerances, low tolerances, and mid-range tolerances.
- We can learn to work with, manage, and expand our windows.

So, how does this help me as a new runner? Great question. To illustrate this, I thought it might be helpful to share an example from my life.

A Bucket List Thing

I have done some downhill skiing in my time; however, I have never cross-country skied. It was a bucket list thing. I wanted to try it. It seemed like another great way to get outside, be active, and enjoy nature. After the hustle and bustle of the Holidays my husband and I packed our bags and drove the four hours or so to a ski area that eats, sleeps, and breathes cross-country skiing.

As a complete beginner – with no idea what to expect – I read some blogs and checked out a couple of YouTube videos. Reflecting on my window of tolerance, at this point, I felt excited. This was something I had wanted to do for a while. There was a sense of adventure – a helpful feeling for me. I also felt happy. We were ready for a couple of days away together exploring new places – we had some cool hikes planned too. Doing an internal scan, I felt well within my window of tolerance.

We arrived at our destination. Refreshed, after a good night's sleep, we were ready to head out to the ski area. We drove to the location, found somewhere to park, ready to head inside to check things out. As we arrived, there were a decent amount of people outside skiing, getting ready to ski, chatting – generally having a good time. I noticed my mind beginning to churn, "Everyone looks like they know *exactly* what they are doing." I felt my energy shift a bit in an upward direction. "No worries," I thought to myself.

As we walked inside, there were even more people chatting – boots, skis, poles, coffee, food, beer. I felt unsure and confused; not sure where to go or what to do. It was that deer in the headlights feeling. I noticed my energy shift below my window of tolerance.

I took a moment, grabbed a breath, and looked around to get my bearings. Then I heard a voice, "Hey, are you guys wanting to ski today?" Yes! Before I knew it we were laughing and joking as we got fitted for boots, skis, and poles. Okay, I was back in my window, feeling more comfortable, thinking, "This is going to be fun; I've totally got this…"

As first-timers, we signed-up for a fifteen-minute 'lesson'. How hard can this be – right? With boots on, skis and poles in hand, and directions to, "Get your skis on and warm-up the knees and ankles a bit" we headed outside.

It was an absolutely beautiful day. The mountains, providing the backdrop, were breathtaking. The sky – clear, crisp, blue – complemented the sparking snow-covered earth in a way that took my breath away. At this point, I was feeling great – comfortable, appropriately excited – and immensely grateful to be right here, right now on such a lovely day.

Our instructor arrived and introduced himself. Nice guy. Super fit, a great skier, and probably half my age. "We've got fifteen minutes to learn the basics," he chimes. "Right, time is ticking; focus," I reminded myself.

We quickly got down to business. "The first things on the agenda are to learn how to stop, how to fall, and how to get back up," he says. Before I know it, my husband's skis are in the air and his bottom is on the ground. "Ahh," I thought, "perfect timing!"

As I pulled my head out of the clouds and back down to earth, a new reality set in. "Yeah, this is going to be way harder than it looks," I thought. As that thought floated through my brain, I noticed my system start to shift above my window of tolerance. More thoughts were coming thick and fast, my heart rate increased. I noticed heat building in my body. And a knot was beginning to congregate in the chest area. "What the heck is this about?" I asked myself. "A part of you is afraid of falling and breaking or injuring something," another part of me responded. "Ahh, that makes sense," I reassured myself. "It must be connected to my broken wrist."

I had two realizations. I was surprised at feeling scared to do something I so wanted to do. And, I recognized that the fear I was feeling had the very real potential of pushing me too far above my window of tolerance. I was in danger of creating a barrier that could limit my ability to learn and reduce my chance of building a sustainable habit.

As a mental health clinician, with over a decade of clinical practice – I quickly recognized the problem. I knew I needed to get a grip and help move my system back down, closer to my window of tolerance. I began to pull out some tools from my personal tool kit. **Helpful Hint**: When you are outside your window of tolerance, knowledge is power. The faster you recognize that your system is shifting, the faster – and more successful – you'll be at getting back into your window.

Because I recognized what was happening and could acknowledge what this was about (my what? and my why?). I was able to employ the breath – always my first line of defense (the breath is a powerful tool – backed by a ton of science which is beyond the scope of this book).

It was these three moves: identifying my what? My why? And finding my breath that helped my system shift, quickly, back toward my window. As I came back into my window, I was able to think more clearly. I knew I had to do one more thing – externalize what, up to this point, was all internal. In short, I had to get what was swirling around in my head out of my mouth. I explained to the instructor, who at this point was urging me to go faster, that "I am on the other side of a broken wrist, which resulted in surgery, after literally a ridiculous slip, while out on the trail a couple of months ago." I also added that, "I am a bit scared of falling" – yes, an understatement for sure; it still counts as saying something. Ironically, he pulls up his sleeve and proudly shares an identical scar from his broken wrist/surgery experience. I am still not sure if that was helpful or not.

Recap: So now we have...

My what?

My why?

Breath.

Externalize (this can be done in several ways – to be discussed later).

Next, I needed an actionable mental plan. I decided that my best line of defense was to adjust my thoughts, focus, breathe, go at my own pace, find my feet, and trust that my confidence will build. For me – based on who I am as a human – these are all reasonable, doable, actionable steps. So, that's exactly what I did. By the end of the day I was:

- Feeling more confident (positive feeling = internal reward).
- Whipping along nicely, loving every moment (positive feeling = internal reward).
- Totally in my window of tolerance (system feeling comfortable = internal reward).

Even though I fell several times, and was clearly still in total newbie status, that didn't matter. I was hooked and eager to do it all over again (internal motivation = powerful intrinsic reward to repeat the behavior).

The point I am making here is that being above, or below, your window of tolerance while trying to learn a new sport, build a new habit, or create a new behavior – is a recipe for disaster. Think about it – if I am scared and anxious, I won't be able to think clearly, my body will be tense making it more likely that I will fall and hurt myself. Hey presto, my biggest fear comes to bite me in the ass (no pun intended). Plus, my brain will create thoughts like, "Dude, what are you doing? This is NO fun!" Thoughts like this will work against me reducing motivation, making it unlikely that I will want to repeat the experience.

"Okay, this is all great for you and cross-country skiing, but what about me as a new or starting over runner?" I hear you ask. Good question. Because we all have various windows of tolerance, once you figure out your personal running habit window you can begin to build running, walking, or any other behavior – based on your unique needs.

What does that mean? This means you get to shape and build the desired behavior in a pleasurable, comfortable, mindful way – increasing the likelihood that you will: repeat, and repeat, and repeat that behavior – until it becomes part of your fabric; automatically something you do with little thought. Also known as a habit. And, this is the cool part, when you *don't* perform that behavior, it feels odd; like something is missing.

In my example all the steps you need have been introduced. Here's the breakdown again:

- My what?
- My why?
- My breath.
- Externalize.
- Actionable Plan.
- Reward.

As you look at these steps start thinking about yourself and the behavior you want to build or restart – in this case, we are talking about running.

Building Your Running Habit

The next couple of pages provide a map for you to follow so you can begin to build your running habit. As an aside, I have used this method to build several behaviors that I now consider ingrained (habit): yoga, meditation, running, hiking, writing, and business practices, such as accounting, banking, billing (things I don't particularly enjoy – yet, they are still part of my routine).

These steps have been effective for me and many of the people I have worked with. However, I also remind clients – and myself – that there is no magic bullet. Yes, even though you will have a great map at your disposal, your journey will still include good days and bad days. Days when you'll feel like, "Yeah, I'm getting this..." and days when you'll feel frustrated with the whole idea. When these thoughts/feelings hit, please remember – this is useful – feelings are *signs of progress* – signs that things are beginning to change in your body and brain. *Keep it up!*

It's also helpful to remember that we have science on our side. As humans we are more similar than we are different. Let me say that again – *we are more similar than we are different.* This means that your system (think biology) and my system (again, think biology) are generally comparable. Trust me, I do not possess any special superpower. If I can figure this habit stuff out, you can figure it out too. Lastly, please note, that not one person on this planet comes out of the chute walking, running, mediating, or writing. We *all* have countless day ones, day twos, and day threes before we reach our desired goals.

What follows is an opportunity to create your personal habit-building map. The exercises are designed for you to build a map based on your needs, your goals, and your personality. So, get that pen and paper out. Let's get focused. It's time to get busy.

Creating Your Map

First, I am going to ask some questions. This will help you have a better understanding about your unique window of tolerance specific to running. Then, yep – you've guessed it – I'll ask more questions as we flesh out your personal steps. Lastly, we'll merge it all together to create your own individualized map. Then…? Well, the rest is up to you, my friend.

The task here is to figure out when you are above, below, and within your window of tolerance. This is going to take some self-reflection. I will ask questions and offer personal examples, tips, and helpful hints along the way to guide you through the process. Take your time. As the questions are presented be ready to notice any thoughts and/or images that may come-up. I have added some blank space for notes and reflections. Please remember, there is no right/wrong, good/bad, or competition here. I don't care about "What Bob did" or "What Gabby's doing" – I am only interested in what makes sense to *you*. P.S. This is great for walkers too…

Okay, ready? Grab a notepad and pen. Here we go.

Imagine a Window

Yes, literally. Close your eyes and imagine a window…

…there are some things we need to learn about our windows.

Welcome to your first reflection point. This exercise will help you begin to understand the space *above* your window. Read and think about the following questions. Remember to put any judgement aside – there are no right or wrong answers here.

The trick is to think back to other times when you have tried to build a habit – any habit – and reflect on what makes you comfortable/uncomfortable as a human. **Tip**: Being above your window includes what I call hot or red feelings. Feelings like frustration, overwhelm, anxiety, stress, etc. **Helpful Hint**: Think about this in terms of the here and now. **Personal Example**: One of my biggest fears was falling and breaking something.

Exercise: To understand what might push you above your window of tolerance answer the following questions.

In general, my biggest fears in life are?

1.

2.

3.

What am I most anxious about when it comes to building this running habit?
*Helpful Hint: Every new behavior/habit has a downside. **Personal Example**: When I started to run longer distances, I had kids. I remember worrying about the extended time away from home. How would people cope? What if something bad happened? In general, these anxieties were 'stories' I was creating for myself. None the less – fact or fiction – these anxieties felt very real to me. **Tip**: Our 'stories' can become barriers. It's important to uncover them.*

1.

2.

3.

I think the three worst things about building this habit will be:
Helpful Hint: Nothing is perfect in this world. Even when we 'love' doing something there's a downside.
Personal Example*: Although I love trail running I don't particularly enjoy driving to the trailhead and the plethora of bugs that go hand in hand with hot, humid summers.*

1.

2.

3.

When I feel like giving-up I generally _____
*Helpful Hint: On this journey, there will be moments when you will want to give-up. It's likely there have been points in your life where you have given-up on something. **Tip**: Knowledge is power. It's important to understand what's going on inside when you feel like giving-up.*

1.

2.

3.

How do you feel when you feel motivated? What's happening in your body/mind?
*Hopefully you have a recent example to work from, if not no worries. **Helpful Hint**: Take a breath and close your eyes for a moment. Think back to a time when*

you did feel motivated. Re-connecting with that time/place will help you answer this question.

1.

2.

3.

Notes and Reflections

I know I am above my window when...?

Now, read and think about the following questions to begin to understand the space *below* your window. At the risk of being redundant, remember – there are no right or wrong answers here. **Tip**: Being below your window includes what I call cool or blue feelings: generally blah, shutdown, like you want to crawl under a rock.

What might push me below my window?

Exercise: To understand what might push you below your window of tolerance answer the following questions.

Things that generally make me feel like I want to shutdown are:
*Helpful Hint: Consider biological processes – tired, hungry, scared, lonely, etc. **Personal Example**: Probably my number one answer is when I feel tired.*

1.

2.

3.

What happens in my body/mind when I feel overwhelmed? List three things with clear examples.

Helpful Hint: We all feel overwhelmed at times. For some this can produce an above the window energy. For others it kicks us into shutdown mode (below window response). Tip: As you build your running/walking habit, it is important to understand how your system is likely to respond when you feel overwhelmed.

1.

2.

3.

What happens in my body/mind when I feel disappointed? List three examples.

Helpful Hint: When building any new behavior there will be moments when you will feel disappointed with something. Maybe you planned to run, but ended up on the couch instead. Tip: Remember two things: 1) this two-steps-forward, three-steps-back feeling is part of the process, and 2) be kind to yourself; internal beratement is not helpful.

1.

2.

3.

My worst fear about building a running habit is:

*Helpful Hint: Fear is a natural part of our emotional climate. Fear is helpful – until it's not. **Personal Example**: The fear I felt about falling could have easily created an emotional barrier stopping me from* *trying a new sport.* **Tip**: *Fear will be present; you can learn to manage it.*

1.

2.

3.

When my mind/body feels like it is in shutdown mode three things that help me feel better are:
Helpful Hint: *Feeling like we want to crawl under a rock happens. Again, helpful – until it's not.* **Tip**: *Remember, knowledge is power. Having some tools in your tool belt that will help you climb back into your window of tolerance is vital in the habit-building process.*

1.

2.

3.

Notes and Reflections

I know I am below my window when...?

Now it's time to find out what keeps you within your window of tolerance. **Tip**: Being in your window of tolerance is like being in the 'green zone' with calm, grounded energy.

Exercise: To learn what gets you back to and keeps you within your window of tolerance answer the following questions.

Some people, places, things that generally make me feel safe are:
Helpful Hint: Reflect on when you feel safest. **Tip:** *It's okay to search back through your memories.*

1.

2.

3.

When I feel calm, balanced, and grounded I notice these things happening in my body/mind:
Helpful Hint: For some people, this might be a difficult question to answer. I suggest some self-reflective journaling or simply keep a log for a couple of days, notice when your system feels calm; note what's going on around you.

1.

2.

3.

If I feel like my system is beginning to shutdown, I will try _____ to bring energy back into my body.
Helpful Hint: Beginning to notice how this 'shutdown' energy feels in your body/mind is a helpful life skill, regardless.

1.

2.

3.

If I feel like my system is getting too activated, I will try _____ to sooth myself.
Helpful Hint: This builds on the above. The ability to recognize activation and then self-sooth – if needed – is another helpful life skill.

1.

2.

3.

List three positive statements I will make about myself as I build this behavior.
Helpful Hint: Our thoughts have a direct influence on our feelings. And our feelings have a direct influence on the actions we choose to take. Having some helpful affirmations (thoughts) we can turn to can be useful in getting us back into our windows.

1.

2.

3.

Notes and Reflections

I know I am within my window when...?

Great work! Now you have some solid information about your personal window it's time to add the finer details specifically related to building your running habit. By the time you have completed the following section you will have your own personal plan. Again, this is about you. I call this the WW-BEAR plan – no particular reason, other than the acronym just works.

The key here is to think about what is true for *you* right now. It's important to remember that things are constantly changing, including our own personal truths. If something is not working for you, you can review, reflect, and make changes. Your WW-BEAR plan is designed to grow and change with you. You can update, add to, and change your WW-BEAR plan over and over again. Go to https://katechampionauthor.com/resources/ for your printable WW-BEAR plan. Right! Let's get started.

Your WW-BEAR Plan

Answer the following questions with your best truth in mind.

W – My what?

> *Helpful Hint: Think about what you would like to get from building this running habit.*

W – My why?

> *Helpful Hint: Reflect on your why. Why do you want to build this running habit?*

B – My breath… This one is so important.

Helpful Hint: *Right now – without thinking – notice where your breath is in your body.*

Upper chest ____

Lower chest ____

Stomach ___

Lower stomach __

Other ____

E – Externalize: What are three ways you can express – let out, get out, or verbalize – these feelings?

Helpful Hint: *As you build this habit you will experience difficult feelings – fear, insecurity, frustration, disappointment, etc. To whom could you express these feelings?* **Tip**: *This could include a safe supportive Facebook group.*

1.

2.

3.

4. To whom:

A – Actionable Plan: List and explain at least three reasonable, doable, actionable steps.

Helpful Hint: *When you notice your system slipping out of your window of tolerance – and it will – you will need a mental action plan to help shift the system back into your window.* **Personal Example**: *You can* *see that I adjusted my thoughts, grounded my body, and focused on slowing my breathing down.*

1.

2.

3.

R – Reward: No skipping this step... List at least one reward in the categories provided that are meaningful and realistic for you.

*Helpful Hint: Reward, whether it's internal (good feelings, positive thoughts, etc.) or external (verbal recognition, a high five, etc.) reward is a powerful component of reinforcing behavior. **Personal Example**: Fun, sense of accomplishment, motivated, excited.*

My internal reward is:

My external reward is:

A big reward is:

A small reward is:

Putting it All Together

If you are still with me at this point... awesome! Now – you've guessed it – it's time to merge your plans, answers, and reflections together to create your own personal window of tolerance – also affectionately known as your habit-building map.

The first map provides an example based on my skiing experience. The italics indicate my personal responses. Following my map is a blank example for you to complete.

Helpful Hint: When I am within my window of tolerance my body and brain feel good. My system likes this – evidenced by feelings of excitement, positive thinking – 'can do' thoughts. And – more importantly – 'want to do' energy is created. When I am outside my window of tolerance, my body and brain are feeling overwhelmed, stuck, and shutdown. This creates a flow of grumbly, "I can't do this…" thoughts – which creates "Why bother; what's the point?" energy.

These are important concepts. Both states are very real and will have a direct effect on whether I am likely to try – you can fill in the blank here – or not try; in this case running, again. Go to https://katechampionauthor.com/resources/ for your printable Habit-Building Map.

Habit-Building Map – Personal Example

My WW-BEAR		Managing my window
What? *Cross-country skiing* **Why?** *It's on my bucket list; something I have always wanted to do…* **Breathe** – *deeper, slower breaths into my lower stomach help* **Externalize** – *verbalize what I am feeling/thinking (worried, frustrated, etc.)* **Actionable steps** (to get me back into my window) • *Slow down* • *Notice I am feeling uncomfortable* • *Breathe* • *Remember my why* • *Keep trying* **Reward** – *fun, sense of accomplishment, motivated, excited*	**I am above my window when:** *I'm feeling scared* *I am thinking I might get injured* *I notice that pit in my stomach* **I am in my window when:** *My breath is calm* *My body feels grounded* *My thoughts are positive and helpful* *I can verbalize what's going on in my head* **I am below my window when:** *I am overly tired* *When I feel blah* *When I'm injured and can't exercise*	Here you are adding your items that are likely to get you back into your window and on track again **When I am above my window I will:** • *Breathe* • *Remember my why* • *Slow down my thinking* • *Ground myself by feeling my feet in my boots* **When I am below my window I will:** • *Use positive affirmations* • *Ask for support* • *Recall my what, and my why* • *Bargain with myself – "just 10 minutes" I can do anything for 10 minutes – right?*

Habit-Building Map

My WW-BEAR

What?

Why?

Breathe –

Externalize –

Actionable steps (to get me back into my window)
-
-
-
-
-

Reward –

I am above my window when:

I am in my window when:

I am below my window when:

Managing my window
Here you are adding your items that are likely to get you back into your window and on track again

When I am above my window I will:
-
-
-
-
-
-

When I am below my window I will:
-
-
-
-
-
-

Plan For Success

In the beginning phases of building a habit it's vital to have a plan for when your motivation and/or willpower waxes and wanes – which it will. Now it's time to learn how to navigate those bumps in the road. Here are a couple of scenarios designed to demonstrate how you can manage your window.

Think about two scenarios that are likely to pull you away from your habit-building process (also known as barriers). Then, using the information from your window, create a plan that will keep you on your road to success. To get you started, I will lead with a personal example. Again, this information is based on my previous scenarios.

Plan for Success: My Personal Example

Scenario A (barrier):

> I plan to run after I get home from work. I'm tired. My thoughts are telling me, "You're tired. Just sit on the couch for a while. You don't need to go for a run."

My plan for success:

> 1. Make sure I have my running shoes by the door.
> 2. Commit to running for ten minutes regardless. Then I can sit on the couch if I still feel like it.

Okay, your turn...

Plan for Success:

Scenario A:

Identify a potential barrier to your success.

Your plan for success *(list two actions)*:

1.

2.

Scenario B:

List another potential barrier to success.

Your plan for success *(list two actions)*:

1.

2.

Congratulations! Your habit-building map is complete. In your hands you have a map based on your unique personality and a plan that accounts for the inevitable bumps you will encounter along the way. Plus, you have a deeper understanding about your inner workings (thoughts, feelings, motivations, etc.). Practice and rehearse your plan. Mentally walking yourself through your plan in your imagination, or in your mind's-eye, before you actually need it, is a powerful tool in the habit-building process.

Again, knowledge is power. Use this information to work *for* you, rather than allowing unhelpful, unconscious, conditioned processes to work against you. Now, lace-up – and get out there!

SECTION III

Top 10 Tips with Sage Advice

Top 10 Tips with Sage Advice

"You don't have to run; you get to run. You were born to run. Never lose the sense of fun and play in your running. If it feels like work, you are doing it wrong."

– Richard B.

IN THIS SECTION you'll find ten solid tips. No artificial intelligence or computer-generated data here. These tips came directly from your peers – real runners – road and trail warriors who have been exactly where you stand today.

To be clear, I don't want to suggest that I am a newbie runner. I have been running for longer than I care to remember. So, of course, I have my own tips. Additionally, I also knew I could do a Google search for the *10 Top Tips for New Runners* – which, of course, I did. That search returned 3,820,000 results. In my heart, my experiences coupled with a Google search, just didn't seem like it would cut it. I know that if I were starting out, or starting over, I would want to hear from real people; actual runners who have learned by trial and error, who can connect with what I am experiencing – in my mind, that's where the real expertise lies.

The Process

One December morning, I went to my trusted Facebook groups and posted this question, "What is the one tip you would give a newbie runner?" That post received 598 comments. I was surprised and touched by two things. First, the sheer number of people who responded, and two, it was the depth, sincerity, and the outpouring of heartfelt support within those communities that had the biggest impact. Even though it wasn't about me, I felt – maybe for the first time – that I actually had a community of likeminded people out there rooting for me. It was powerful.

This is why I dedicated this book to you and the running community. It's my way of giving back and sharing that sense of unity, encouragement, and support – also a vital component in building any sustainable habit.

I had not anticipated the number of responses those Facebook posts would attract, which also meant that I hadn't considered how I would organize that amount of data. To give you some context, as I mentioned earlier, my 'one tip' question went out to eleven Facebook groups. I received almost 600 comments over the period of a week. Clearly, my Post-it note method of organization wouldn't cut it...

I put my researcher hat on – I knew all those years struggling in statistics classes would pay off. I whipped-up an Excel spreadsheet. I created themes, which formed categories. Then I recorded the number of responses in each category. From there it was pretty simple to organize the data by greatest to least number of responses. If your eyes are glazing over at this point, I totally get it. The bottom line: this is not a scientific study. However, the tips below are crafted from actual input from real – road and trail – runners. The data was arranged in order of importance (#1 being the top tip) using a loose research-based method.

Along with these great tips, this process also harvested a wealth of helpful knowledge and advice. This section ties – the general knowledge, the advice, and the practical tips – together allowing a deeper dive. You will see the *sage advice* in direct quotes. These are direct quotes, followed by the runners first name, last initial, and their Facebook affiliation. As we take a look at each tip, remember in habit building, knowledge is power. Your job is to use this section as your *go to* resource as you begin to build or re-build your running habit.

The Top 10

Tip 1: Proper shoes

Tip 2: Start slow/build slow

Tip 3: Have fun – don't focus on speed, time, distance, etc.

Tip 4: Don't compare yourself to others

Tip 5: Be patient with yourself

Tip 6: Remember to cross-train (strength training, yoga, etc.)

Tip 7: Be mindful about your surroundings (rocks, roots, cars, etc.)

Tip 8: Listen to your body

Tip 9: Warm-up, cool-down, stretch

Tip 10: Find a community

A Deeper Dive

Tip 1 – Proper shoes

Shoes are a huge deal. I remember when I started out, the first thing my friend did was send me to my local running store to get properly fitted for running shoes – boy, that decision has made a huge difference.

Why are the right shoes so important? Whether you or are running, walking, run/walking, a trail or a road lover, heading out for your first mile or 100 miles – problems like blisters, shin splints, tendonitis, planter fasciitis, knee, and hip pain can be avoided, and often reversed, with well-fitting running shoes that are a good match for your body and running style.

If you decide to heed this advice and head over to your local running store, what can you expect? Lots of questions... Be prepared for questions like: Are you a runner, walker, or a run/walker? How many miles do you anticipate running/walking per week? Do you run on mostly road, trail, or are you a hybrid runner? Do you have a history of injuries?

Also be ready, and willing, to have your gait analyzed. Most running shoe stores will offer a complimentary gait analysis. This is an important part of the process. A gait analysis will determine how your feet and ankles actually work as you run/walk. Once your gait, injury profile, and running preferences have been assessed, that information will be used to determine the best shoe based on your particular needs.

Then you'll be offered the opportunity to try out a couple of the recommended shoe options. This is when you get to play... Be thinking about fit. How do the shoes feel on your feet? Walk/run around. Some stores have an indoor track – don't be shy or feel rushed – take those shoes out for a spin.

Finding the right shoe based on your unique needs is also an important part of the habit-building process. If your shoes are ill fitting, causing discomfort, or just don't 'feel right' – trust me, this will become a barrier – pushing you out of your window of tolerance and away from the habit you are working so hard to build.

> *Sage Advice:*
>
> "First discover what's the proper shoe that works for you. Very important!!! When I started running someone gave me her used shoes and I was happy, I didn't have to buy shoes. I kept complaining about pain in my knees and ankle until I realized it was the shoes. They were worn out and not a good fit for my gait. So, yeah! Shoes are very important!"
>
> *– Naomi R (Trail and Ultra Running Group)*
>
> "Go to your local running shop and let them fit you properly."
>
> *– Mike W (Back of the Pack Athlete Community)*

Tip 2 – Start slow/build slow

Whether you are fresh off the couch or starting over, remember – it will take time for your body to adjust to this new way of moving. As an aside, in my gut I believe humans are engineered to run; and run long distances. Dennis Bramble professor of biology at the University of Utah and anthropologist Daniel Lieberman from Harvard University concur. In a study published in 2004, they conclude: "Running has substantially shaped human evolution. Running made us human – at least in an anatomical sense. We think running is one of the most transforming events in human history."

If we are 'born to run', why are we plagued with so many injuries? Here are a couple of possible reasons: waiting until adulthood to pick-up that running habit, running on artificial surfaces, and the proliferation of high-tech running shoes may have detrimental effects on our biomechanics, increasing our risk of injury – more on this in the Preventing Injuries section.

To mitigate the likelihood of strains and sprains and increase your chances of creating a sustainable running habit, many coaches and habit-building gurus, recommend a slow build with a combination of walking/running/walking. Interestingly, this intersects nicely with the habit-building science, where the power of a slow build: taking small steps, frequently, over an extended period of time, is recommended. Remember the classic saying, 'Rome wasn't built in a day'? – yeah, sound advice, my friends.

The question to ask yourself right now is, "What can I *realistically* do on a *regular* basis?" Note the language here. When it comes to habit building – *regular* means every other day – at minimum, and *realistic* means finding a starting point where *you* are comfortable. If this means a regular walk to the mailbox and back – that's wonderful. Celebrate!

Starting where you are comfortable could be as simple as committing to walking around the block every other day. Some people might consider a walk/run combination – starting slowly with a warm-up walk to get the blood and oxygen moving, followed by a couple of minutes of easy jogging, then back to walking. This cycle can be repeated initially for ten or fifteen minutes then gradually increased from there. Check-out the Preventing Injuries section. Suggestions for specific programs/books/and groups that may be helpful can be found at: https://katechampionauthor.com/resources/

Helpful Hint:

- Start with what you can comfortably do
- Get out there, at least, every other day. This is important, so I am going to say it again, "get out there every other day" – even if it's for five minutes. This step is vital for both the brain, and the body, so

they can begin working – behind the scenes – to create the complex network of neural associations they need so you can build the habit you want.

Sage Advice:

"Just do it!!! Which ever you fancy first [road or trail], then try the other. I hate roads with all the fumes and noise. I love trails and countryside views but whatever gets you out there. Take it easy. Begin to build your strength and stamina. Most of all run happy…"

-- *Chris G (Forever Runners over 50)*

"Slow and Steady."

-- *David K (Back of the Pack Athlete Community)*

"Progress slowly, especially if you are already in shape… Your legs might not be able to keep up with your cardio capacity and ambition; you'll get injured."

– *Greg W (Ultra Running Group)*

Tip 3 – Have fun – don't focus on speed, time, distance, etc.

When we think about children the importance of play and playing is a no-brainer. Unfortunately, as we transition into adulthood we seem to lose natural concepts like having fun, exploring, creating, and being curious – basic elements of our nature.

One of the cool things about running is that it can connect or reconnect us with our childhood selves. Take a moment to think about how you moved as a child. If, for some reason, you don't have access to these memories – no worries – go and visit a park or a playground, watch the children as they move around, run, and use their bodies. Whether you are recalling personal memories or observing others: study their faces, listen to the sounds they make. What might they be thinking? How might they be feeling? Can you recreate that in your body and/or mind?

For many, having fun also means leaving the technology at home, not comparing yourself to other people, and not tracking your speed, distance, or time. I don't care if you are starting out at a snail's pace. In this phase of the habit-building process it's all about allowing the brain/body to build strong – pleasurable – neural associations. It's your job is to keep it light, simple, and fun.

Sage Advice:

"One step at a time. A mile is a mile no matter what the time is…"

– Robert S (Ultra Running Group)

"Don't set lofty goals in the beginning; stay slow and steady."

– Ellen B (Slow Runners Club Walk/Run)

Tip 4 – Don't compare yourself to others

The ability to compare is extremely helpful if you were part of the early human hunter gatherer community. Today, in the 21st century, although our lives are vastly different, our deep impulses to compare have not adapted to account for things like technology, social media, consumerism, sprawling urban areas, and our 7 billion tribal mates.

The fact is, we are wired to measure ourselves against others. According to experts who study social comparison, the ability to compare is an evolutionary mechanism stemming from the need to protect from and assess threat. In other words, comparison is a survival mechanism. Experts also suggest that our desire to compare is one of the ways we develop a deeper understanding of who we are and where our strengths and values lie. Comparison can also function as a protective checks and balances mechanism.

Great, we've established that the ability to compare is deeply wired into our DNA. How does this relate to building a sustainable running habit? There are two sides to the comparison coin. On one side our natural propensity to compare can be helpful. For instance, through comparing we can feel inspired by someone else's accomplishments, which can stir up motivation to improve or start something new. Additionally, let's be honest, when we compare and we recognize, or perceive, that in some areas, we might be a notch above our neighbor, co-worker, or fellow runner that can provide a boost in our self-esteem, which feels good.

The other side of the comparison coin is not so helpful for building that sustainable running habit. To illustrate, here's an example: Imagine taking a walk through the park. You are thinking about your health, fitness, and wanting to make some improvements. Seemingly, out of nowhere, a very fit, trim runner passes you effortlessly – no sweat, no huffing and puffing, no grunting, no groaning. You watch them as they glide past you like a proud gazelle, then off they go into the distance. What do you think that comparison part of your brain is doing in that moment? Here are a couple of common unhelpful comparison type themes that may arise:

- Fitness level – "Geez, I'm so out of shape."
- Age – "I've got ten years on her/him."
- Time – "I have no time – with the kids, family, job…"
- Aspirations – "I'll never be able to run like that; I'm just too…"

In the early stages of the habit-building process, comparisons like this are not helpful. Be on the lookout for these thoughts, themes, and situations. Focus on people that are a good match for *you* based on where *you* are in *your* process. Seek energy that feels supportive and positive. In this beginning phase it's important to stay focused on your personal improvements. Remember – the only person you should be comparing yourself to is – YOU!

Sage Advice:

"My tip is that every runner is unique. Find what works for you. Don't be afraid to experiment. What's in one month, will be out the next. No one has the answers but you."

– Troy B (Ultra Running Group)

"Race yourself – not those around you. Progress over perfection…"

– Erin C (Slow Runners Club Walk/Run)

"Don't compare yourself to others. Comparison is truly the thief of joy."

– Elizabeth O (Slow Runners Club Walk/Run)

Tip 5 – Be patient with yourself

We've all heard the old adage, 'patience is a virtue'. Today, the power of patience is well supported by science. When it comes to building a sustainable habit, patience is vital. According to researchers from the Health Behavior Research Centre in London, habits are defined as "actions that are triggered automatically in response to contextual cues that have been associated with their performance." Putting on a seatbelt (action) after getting into the car (cue) and brushing our teeth (action) before going to bed (cue) are two common examples.

What is the opposite of patience? Impatience. What are the feelings that go hand-in-hand with impatience? Agitation, frustration, disappointment. When, in your mind, changes are not happening fast enough these types of thoughts and feelings have the potential to move you above or below your window of tolerance.

The ability to be patient in the early steps of the habit-building process is crucial because creating sustainable habits take time. Our everyday lives are profoundly influenced by habits. Think about your day. Everything from your morning routine, to your lunch choices, to your decision to sit on the couch or go for that run are powerfully influenced by the neural associations, or habits, your brain has developed. Now try to intentionally disrupt one of those habits. It's difficult. However, deconstructing old habits and creating new habits is 100% possible when you harness the power of time, repetition, and patience.

Sage Advice:

"You likely won't win the race but you can win the mental game."

– Sally K (Ultra Running Group)

"Just do it. Again and again. It keeps getting better…"

– Van T (Back of the Pack Athlete Community)

"Being able to finish a race/run where everything did not go to plan is much more rewarding than finishing the perfect race/run."

– Henk K (Ultra Running Group)

Tip 6 – Remember to cross-train (strength training, yoga, etc.)

This great piece of advice is 100% backed by science. In a comprehensive review of twenty-six studies which looked at the use of strength training – free weights, weight machines, and/or body resistance – in a range of recreational to highly trained professional runners, researchers found athletes reported measured improvements in several areas including: stiffness during running and non-running tasks, general performance gains, improvements in the quadricep muscles, lean leg mass, and running economy.

Helpful Hint:

Multi-joint exercises using free weights were more effective compared to weight machines.

If, in the back of your mind, you are groaning, imagining the agony of days, weeks, and years spent hoofing it to the gym, there's good news – strength training a couple of times a week over a six to nine-week period was enough to enhance running performance in both recreational and highly trained runners. The review concludes by stating that "runners of any training status can benefit from strength training." How cool is that!

Sage Advice:

"Hit the gym and lift on a regular basis, preferably a program with built-in progression."

— *Scot H (Back of the Pack Athlete Community)*

"For trail, make sure you strengthen your ankles first and work on balance. Lots of rolled ankles on the trails. And, also learn how to fall – tuck and roll – so when you fall, and you will, you won't break a wrist. Also wear orange on the trails during hunting season. Finally, enjoy every second of it!"

— *Jenny W (Running, Training, and Motivation Group)*

Tip 7 – Be mindful about your surroundings (rocks, roots, cars, etc.)

Let me clarify. There is a difference between mindful running and being mindful about your surroundings. Mindful running is linked to the practice of meditation – a technique for deepening awareness, settling the thoughts, strengthening the mind – offering us a break from the mental stress of our constant internal chatter.

Being mindful about your surroundings is – bottom line – about safety. Whether you are on the trail, the track, or the road – safety always comes first. What does this mean? For road runners this means being aware of where you are, who's around, noticing that car approaching, the uneven sidewalk, the dog sniffing around, out on its own adventure.

For trail runners this means knowing where you're going and how the heck you're going to get back. It means being mindful about time, daylight, and weather. It includes watching out for rocks, roots, scree, and low-hanging tree limbs. Personal experience talking here – I have been lost, taken by surprise, unprepared for the weather, tripped, fallen, and slipped more times than I care to admit.

Four safety tips all runners should consider:

Find an anchor person: Always let someone know where you are going and when you plan to be back. As a solo runner, I have a couple of people I send a quick text to – I feel more confident knowing someone on the planet knows where I am and will call for help if needed.

Trust your gut: As humans we were once experts at trusting our instincts. It's time to reconnect and sharpen that skill. If something or someone feels 'off' or 'creepy' or 'out of place' – trust those instincts. Avoid. Avoid. Avoid. Take a different route. Cross the street. Come back at a different time. *Helpful Hint:* The more you practice using your instincts and being aware of the people, places, things around you the more you will sharpen this skill.

Know the location: Let's face it running is a great way to explore a new city, neighborhood, park, or trail. However, be smart. Before you head out consider... What's the neighborhood like? Are there other runners, walkers, kids out and about? Stick to busier areas – bike paths, trails, roads – with more people around. If you're running in an area that is familiar have a couple of 'safe' stops in mind en route. I have a couple of houses and at least one business I know I can stop by if I need to pee or get a drink or take a break. Clearly, this strategy won't work if you're out on the trail – unless you have the luxury of a loop with a shelter house or your car or a park rangers' station strategically placed along the way. For trail be prepared with a map, extra water, a snack, and maybe some toilet paper.

Think about visibility: If you are running on roads visibility is vital. Even if you are doing all the right things: running toward the traffic, obeying cross walk signals, looking both ways before crossing – bad things can happen. Drivers are unpredictable, frequently distracted, and *not* looking for people running or walking. Wearing brightly colored clothing, reflective bands, and a flashing beacon they can see from Mars can certainly be helpful. As can learning to be a defensive runner. Being a defensive runner means assuming vehicles – and their humans – are oblivious to your presence. If you have the option, think about choosing low traffic roads with wide shoulders and few intersections. Yes, I know it sounds drastic – if you haven't read author Stephen King's account of his 'accident' while out walking I encourage you to check out his memoir: *On Writing.*

Sage Advice:

"Trail: no headphones, don't be afraid to walk/hike the hills and rough areas. Work on ankle and hip strength because you will be working different muscles! Road: if it's dark, wear lights or reflective clothing and be defensive around cars. Above all – have fun!"

– Jodi F (Slow Runners Club Walk/Run)

"Trail – expect to fall. Road – don't assume someone sees you."

    – Lisa K (Running, Training, and Motivation Group)

"Trail run with someone. Road, tell a friend where you will be running. Be safe."

    – Marilyn S (Slow Runners Club Walk/Run)

Tip 8 – Listen to your body

I don't know about you, but in my world I often hear, or use, the phrase 'listen to your body'. Recently, during a professional development course, the instructor started the day with a moment of quiet followed by an invitation to "listen to your body. Notice. What is it feeling? Thinking? Saying?"

I also know from my own meditation journey and teaching in the mental health field, the phrase 'listen to your body' can often be met with glazed eyes. It's like, "Body? What body? What the heck are you talking about?" This, in my opinion, is because many of us socialized in Western culture receive little to no education about the importance of – or instruction about *how to* listen to these amazing structures we are living in.

As a new runner, this is a great, and important, time to build this skill. Notice, I used the word *skill*. Look, we can have all the latest gadgets and cool technology on the planet; yet, nothing compares to – or replaces – the value of being your own up close and personal radar detector. By learning how to be dialed into the body, you can become your own personal expert – on you.

Understanding the connection between the mind and the body and the body and the mind is like being able to access a constant stream of information that monitors everything from your thoughts and feelings, to motivations and challenges, to niggles and twinges, to danger and safety, to hydration and dehydration – the list is endless.

Additionally, as a new runner, access to information about what's happening in your body is important. Without it, all the hard work you are putting into building that sustainable habit, could very easily be sabotaged by 'thinking errors' – unhelpful thoughts that arise in the brain – like, "this sucks, I hate running..."

In the early phases of habit building, these thoughts can – and will – pop-up when you are about to lace-up and head out for that run. Or when you are on the way home from work with a plan to stop by the gym. If you can stop for a moment. Notice that thought. Not act on it. Take a breath. Tune your attention into the body and ask, "Okay, what is this really about?" You might discover that the body is tired and the "running sucks" thought is code for the body trying to communicate that it needs a rest day, or some ice cream, or some encouragement. With this information in the front of your mind you can review and self-reflect. You can ask, "Do I need to compromise – run for half the time or walk instead?" "Do I need to suck it up and get over myself?" For me, this would trigger my "No excuses, Missy..." speech, followed by a swift kick in the rear end as I lace-up and head out of the door.

Need a rest day? If you genuinely need a rest day then take one and enjoy it.

Helpful Hint:

Remember not to allow one rest day to turn into two, three, four 'rest days'. One of the golden rules of habit building is – *do not miss more than one day*. Meaning if you skip a day you get right back to it the very next day.

Sage Advice:

"Run both [road and trail] so you can feel the difference and make adjustments on your own..."

– *Generoso P (Ultra Running Group)*

"Stay consistent and listen to your body. If you need to walk, run/walk, do it to build up your endurance."
> – *Ruyayeen R (Slow Runners Club Walk/Run)*

Tip 9 – Warm-up, cool-down, stretch

This tip brings with it a general lack of agreement about the benefits of pre/post run stretch, warm-up and/or cool-down. After doing a bit of digging here's the current thinking on the topic.

Before heading out on that run there is some research suggesting that spending a few minutes warming up your body along with a similar cooling off period post run has some protective benefits. According to researchers, a warm-up helps prepare your body for the physical activity. Warming-up gives your cardiovascular system a heads-up, "Hey, we're on the move; let's get serious." This prompts your cardiovascular system to begin to raise the body's temperature and increase blood flow to the muscles. The cool-down period promotes a gradual return to base line regulating things like heart rate, blood pressure, respiratory system, and body temperature.

A warm-up period has also been shown to help reduce muscle stiffness and soreness. Your warm-up should start just a few minutes before your run/walk. Think about beginning to fire up your large muscle groups (hamstrings, glutes, etc.). Start slowly, gradually increasing your speed and intensity. You'll notice the heart rate, respiratory rate, and temperature begin to build in the body. If you are warming-up for a walk, start with a few minutes of slow walking. Consider adding some shoulder and/or neck rolls along with some arm movement (swinging, circles, etc.). If you're warming-up for a run, then walking briskly for five to ten minutes would be a good place to start.

As for your post run/walk allow five minutes or so for a cool-down period. Start by slowing your pace gradually until you reach your usual walking pace and your breath settles. Over time, as you learn to listen to the body, you will be able to tell when your systems are back to base line. Once your body has stabilized walk for a few more minutes and then give yourself a pat on the back.

As for stretching, the research suggests holding any stretching until after the workout – when your muscles are already warm. Stretching when your muscles are warm has been shown to improve flexibility and range of motion. As far as stretching as a means to help prevent injury – the jury is still out.

> ### Helpful Hint:
>
> Warming up and cooling down is different to stretching. When you warm up/cool-down you are using the whole body to rev up and ramp down systems. Stretching focuses on groups of specific muscles, ligaments, tendons, etc.

> ### Sage Advice:
>
> "Start and finish each run with a walk... it is good to warm the muscles up and down."
>
> *– Julian C (Forever Runners over 50)*
>
> "Vital if you want to keep moving into your 60s, 70s, and beyond..."
>
> *– Kate J (Back of the Pack Athlete Community)*

Tip 10 – Find a community

Why is community important? Consider, for a moment, the root – *common* – and the suffix – *unity* – that together create the word *community*. Community is a common thread that unites. Communities bring people together, providing a sense of belonging, support, safety. A community shares, accepts, advocates, and comforts. Deeply rooted in our psyche, we are driven to seek and build community. A sense of community is an essential part of our wellbeing. As a new, or returning, runner/walker connecting with a community of like-minded people is an important part of the process. Here are some of the benefits communities provide:

- **Support** – mentorship, encouragement, learning from others who have been in your shoes.

- **Connections** – help, personal growth, helping self and others.

- **Inspiration** – exchange of ideas, creativity, experience, and support to *keep going* when you feel like giving-up.

- **Resources** – humans are by nature *inter*-dependent beings. Which is why teams (also a form of community) consistently outpace the guy or gal forging ahead by her/himself.

- **Growth** – through the collective sharing of resources: knowledge, experience, advice – we grow and our communities strengthen.

By nature, I am a bit of a lone wolf. Somewhere, in my journey, I realized the importance – probably because I didn't have one – of community. I craved connection with people like me – later-in-life athletes – who love being outside – running, hiking, backpacking – regardless of speed, finishers' medals, and rankings. I had a gap in my life which I filled by creating the Back of the Pack Athlete (BOPa) Community. The best way to connect to our community is to visit https://backofthepackathlete.com or join us on Facebook at: https://www.facebook.com/backofpack/. In the words of Helen Keller, "Alone, we can do so little; together we can do so much." I hope to see you there!

Sage Advice:

"Running groups are amazing motivation. Meet/start together, then do your own thing. Celebrate the finish of each great run no matter how it turns out. The community is very inspiring."

– Tanya B (Trail and Ultra Running Group)

"This is your journey. Don't compare yourself with others. Surround yourself with positive people…"

– Rae A (Back of the Pack Athlete Community)

SECTION IV

Preventing Injuries

Preventing Injuries

"Healing is a matter of time, but sometimes it's a matter of opportunity."

– Hippocrates

IT'S TRUE, RUNNING – at any pace – is an excellent form of exercise. However, it is also a reality that injuries are common in runners at every level. Interestingly, according to one study, the beginner runner is twice as likely to report an injury when compared to more advanced runners.

Believe me, as a new or returning runner/walker there is nothing more frustrating than beginning to build confidence, momentum – and habit – only to get sidelined by an injury. When I use the word, 'injury' I am not talking about something major – like a broken leg or a head trauma – the chances of that type of injury is slim. I am talking about the niggles in the hip, tweaks in the knee, and discomfort in the foot or calf – the annoying everyday stuff.

The saying, "an ounce of prevention is worth a pound of cure..." could not be more true. The intention of this chapter is to help you stay off the sidelines. Consider the following material your ounce of prevention. Full disclaimer here – I am a runner, writer, mental health professional. I have worked through my own crop of injuries. I have read and researched. However, I am not a specialist in this area. Please know your body, use your best judgement, and never delay in seeking professional help when needed.

Most running-related injuries are due to doing too much too soon and/or overuse. Running injuries fall into two camps: acute and chronic. An example of an acute injury would be a fall followed by lots of blood or a broken bone. This type of injury would clearly need immediate medical attention. Chronic injuries are generally low-grade things. Below is a list of the five top offenders with a brief explanation of the condition, 'what to do...' suggestions, and possible causes so you can take preventative action.

Planter Fasciitis (PF)

What is it?

Estimates suggest that over one million people are affected by PF per year. According to the National Institute of Health (NIH) this condition accounts for 10% of runner related injuries. The biggest symptom indicating possible PF is pain in the bottom of the foot that reaches from the heel to the arch. You may experience discomfort during the early stage of your run/walk. Also, the pain may subside, then return later. This condition can often feel worse first thing in the morning when getting out of bed and after sitting for a while.

Possible causes
- High arches
- Flat feet
- Shoes: worn out, poor fit, incorrect type
- Tight calf muscles
- Too much too soon: too far, too fast
- Poor running form: biomechanics – many experts think that this is the major cause of PF

What to do...

- Rest: consider cross-training – biking, swimming, gym
- Ice: ice the area for twenty minutes two to three times a day
- Stretch: focus on the calf muscles
- Massage: focus on the arch of the foot
- Shoes: check your shoes for fit, wear, etc. (see Tip 1: Shoes)

Iliotibial Band Syndrome (ITB)

What is it?

According to the National Institute of Health (HIH) ITB syndrome is the second most common running related injury with an incident rate, at the high end, of 12%. Imagine a thick bunch of fibers that run from the outside of your hips down the outside of your thigh through your knee down to your shin bone. This is often referred to as the IT band. An ache, tightness, or a burning feeling in the knee, thigh, hip area may indicate problems with your IT band. It seems that repetitive bending and/or stretching of the knee can be linked to IT band syndrome. IT band syndrome can plague newer runners, endurance runners, walkers, and cyclists.

Possible causes

- Lack of adequate warm-up and cool-down routines (see Tip 9: Warming up)
- Going out too hard, too fast (see Tip 2: Start slow)
- Not enough rest between running/walking
- The shoe thing – again!
- Terrain – running on the same side of the road, uneven, or banked (vs. flat) surfaces

- Weak abs, glutes, hip muscles (see Tip 6: Cross-train)
- Biomechanics of your leg, foot, running form

What to do...
- Limiting the offending activity – consider cross-training
- Icing the outside of the knee
- Making sure you have good running/walking form
- Stretching and strengthening with a focus on the hips, thighs, glutes, and knees

Achilles Tendonitis (AT)

What is it?

Over a lifetime AT injuries are strongly associated with sporting activities. For recreational runners, specifically, the prevalence of AT is high, accounting for approximately 9% of cases. Interestingly, according to the National Institute of Health (HIH), males have a higher tendency for AT rupture when compared to females.

Achilles tendonitis is the largest, strongest tendon in the body. Your AT starts in the back of your heel. It connects the heel bone to the calf muscle. The AT is fundamental to walking, jumping, and running. Problems with the AT are indicated by pain when the heel strikes, the foot lands, when running up hill, or with sudden changes in direction. Discomfort may be worse in the morning with your first few steps.

Possible causes
- Overuse: Again, too much too fast
- Excessive hill or stair running/walking
- Tight calf muscles
- Poor running form
- Shoes: Again (see Tip 1: Shoes)

What to do...

- Modify training schedule
- Stretch calf muscles
- Rest, ice, massage
- Physical therapy

Runner's Knee (RK)

What is it?

According to the NIH, in the general population approximately 23% of the population reports problems with RK. Incidences are higher for runners, military personnel, and younger teen athletes.

I recall reading somewhere that there is no such thing as runner's knee. Remember, I am not an expert, however, I have included RK because experts use the term as a broad way of describing general knee pain. The actual medical term is Patellofemoral Pain Syndrome (PPS). Although PPS is not unique to runners it is something a new runner should be aware of. What to look for? Be mindful about any dull pain around the front of the knee area when you are active, pain after sitting for long periods with your knees bent, and any rubbing, clicking, or grinding sounds when bending and/or straightening the knee.

Possible causes

- Overuse – yep, no surprise there
- A direct hit to the knee
- Imbalanced, weak, or tight thigh muscles
- Incorrect, worn or poorly fitting shoes
- Poor biomechanics

What to do...

- Rest; ice
- Strengthen quadriceps and hips (see Tip 6: Cross-training)

- Stretch calves, hammies (aka hamstrings) quadriceps, and very important – hip flexors
- Physical therapy
- Shoes: Review – Refit? Replace?

Shin Splints (SS)

What is it?

The NIH report that incidents of SS in runners range somewhere between 14% and 20%. High volume and impact sports have been cited as risk factors.

The term 'shin splints' also known as Medial Tibial Stress Syndrome (MTSS) is a cumulative stress disorder caused by repeated pounding which overly stresses the bones (shin), muscles, and joints in the lower leg. Shin splints may affect people during moderate to heavy physical activity, people that start, take a break, then pick the sport back up again – think tennis, basketball, running, and/or the new runner. If you are experiencing a dull ache in the front/side of the shin area, pain or tenderness along the inner part of the lower leg, or general muscle pain in those areas, take note, this may be a signal indicating shin splints.

Possible causes

- Weak thigh, glute muscles
- Running on hard surfaces like concrete
- Fast stops and starts as in soccer and downhill skiing
- Poorly fitted/worn out shoes for running or working out
- Lack of flexibility
- Biomechanics – form, training, foot strike, etc.
- Exercising when leg muscles and tendons are overly tired

What to do...

- Rest the legs

- Cross-train: focus on strengthening the calf, hip, thigh, and core muscles (see Tip 6: Cross-train)
- Elevate, ice, compression
- Massage area with a foam roller
- Give your legs enough time to warm-up (see Tip 9: Warm-up)
- Consider shock absorbing insoles
- Start out slow – gradually increasing time on your feet and distance (see Tip 2: Start slow)

Folks. Listen-up. Whether you are running, walking, or walk-running, remember – the goal here is to build a sustainable habit; meaning: this is something that becomes part of your life; a behavior you do for the foreseeable future. Which, in turn means staying healthy. Can you imagine lacing-up well into your 70s and 80s? Yep, it's totally possible. If you haven't read my book *Never Too Late: Inspirational Conversations, Tips, and Sage Advice from 7 Everyday Athletes* who are still rockin' in their 60s, 70s, and 80s – check it out at: https://katechampionauthor.com/book/never-too-late/

BONUS SECTION

Habit Shaper and Willpower Builder

Habit Shaper and Willpower Builder

"All the power is within you; you can do anything and everything; believe in that."
– Swami Vivekananda

A RECENT ARTICLE looking at barriers, and preferences, around physical activity found that people's top three fitness preferences were: walking, running, and jogging. Barriers, or reasons cited as to why people did not walk, run, or jog on a regular basis were: fear of injuries, no time, low energy, and lack of willpower.

In the preceding sections we have covered injury and injury prevention, time and, how in the beginning of the habit building process, your running/walking time must be paired, booked or cued with other established activities such as taking the dog out, collecting the mail, and coming home from work.

We have discussed low energy. I view low energy as being below your window of tolerance – in the blue zone – with that shutdown feeling. We've explored solutions for this such as bargaining with yourself: "Just get those shoes on and head out for five minutes," or predicting low energy; preparing for it and/or problem solving such as considering a different time of day.

Let's be honest. A conversation about building sustainable habits would not be complete without a discussion about willpower. In my mind, not addressing willpower would be a disservice – like lukewarm Starbucks or listening to a comedian who has great stories but no punchlines.

In the previous sections we focused on habits and habit-building. In this Bonus Section we take it one step further by activating the power team. By getting crystal clear about the habits we are working on and by learning how to tap into, and harness, our willpower muscles.

So, what is willpower? The first part of this word – *will* means having the ability to make a conscious choice. When you have 'will' it means you can act or make a choice without being hindered.

Power – the second part of the word – is about the motivation to exercise will. You can see that *will* and *power* are partners, they go hand-in-hand. Willpower is an important ingredient in life. We rely on willpower for many things – everything from exercising regularly to saving money to avoiding fast food to quitting smoking. Willpower can also be described as: determination, self-control, drive, etc. At the heart of willpower is the ability to resist short-term temptations or barriers so we can achieve the more desirable long-term behaviors or habits. Basically, willpower is the ability to consistently push our impulse for instant gratification out of the way in favor of longer-term, more satisfying goals and rewards.

According to the American Psychological Association willpower includes:

- The ability to delay gratification and resist short-term temptations to meet long-term goals.
- The capacity to override an unwanted thought, feeling or impulse.
- The conscious, effortful regulation of the self, by the self.
- A limited resource capable of being depleted.

Your personal Willpower Builder is all about planning for the times; trust me, there will be times when your willpower is low – shutdown and hiding under a rock somewhere. The last point on this list – that willpower is a limited resource – is the main focus of your personal Willpower Builder.

As humans, although we are hardwired for willpower, willpower does not flow in a nice, even, consistent stream instantly accessible at the click of our fingers. Willpower, like everything else in life, ebbs and flows. Our willpower is particularly challenged when we are tired, stressed, hungry, and disorganized.

Thanks to the researchers who study willpower, we know that, like a muscle, willpower can be trained and strengthened. You can probably see this in your day. You get up. Get your gym bag packed with every intention of running after work. Maybe you didn't sleep so well? Maybe you had a particularly challenging customer? Maybe you missed lunch? Maybe the kids were sick and you stayed home to care for them while also trying to work remotely? These common scenarios drain our limited supply of willpower. Despite all our good intentions we are exhausted, we collapse on the couch zoned out in front of the TV, and our running shoes don't see the light of day.

In order to build sustainable habits, we must plan for the inevitable lapses in willpower. The good news is that by planning and strengthening willpower our 'helpful' habits will grow and extend into other areas of our lives. For instance, I know that if I run regularly, I am more likely to eat better, drink more water, and generally be more pleasant to be around. The trick is to plan to fail so we can succeed.

The following section includes what I call the 'power team': your personal Habit Shaper and Willpower Builder. Revisiting the car analogy, think of the habit shaper as the vehicle (providing physical structure). The willpower builder is akin to the gas in the tank (the energy that keeps you going). Remember, building a sustainable habit along with the willpower to drive that habit takes time, baby steps, patience, and a plan for things when they are going well and when they are not going so well. Take some time to complete the following questions as honestly and as thoroughly as possible.

Habit Shaper

(Go to https://katechampionauthor.com/resources/ for your printable Habit Shaper)

Directions: Take some time to answer as honestly and fully as you can. There is no judgement here. No comparison. No right. No wrong. Take a moment – ask yourself, "What matters to me at this point in my life?"

Name:_____

Date:_____

Exercise: To get crystal-clear about your whys and goals.

Why do I want to build this habit?

My long-term fitness goals are:
1.

2.

3.

What are my running/walking micro-steps (mini goals) for...

Next week?

Next month?

Next ninety days?

Next twelve months?

What is the worst thing about not reaching these goals?

What is the best thing about reaching these goals?

Your Concrete Action Plan

Exercise: Identify one small step you will commit to taking every day.

I am committed to:

My plan A:

When: Exact time of day

Before I:

After I:

Location:

My plan B:

When: Exact time of day

Before I:

After I:

Location:

My plan C:

When: Exact time of day

Before I:

After I:

Location:

Congratulations! You now have concrete plans and three flexible options to help you crush any barriers that may arise.

Willpower Builder

(Go to https://katechampionauthor.com/resources/ for your printable Willpower Builder)

The phrase "know thyself" is inscribed on the frontispiece of the Temple of Apollo in Delphi, Greece. In philosophy this phrase postulates that we must live according to our individual nature. Understanding our individual nature is best accomplished through the process of questioning and reflecting. The questions below are designed to better understand and build your willpower muscles.

To me willpower is:

Currently, I already use willpower when:

My willpower is strongest when:

My willpower is weakest when:

What drains my willpower?

What restores my willpower?

Your Plan for Low Willpower

Now you have a better understanding about your personal brand of willpower it's time to make an action plan for when willpower is low.

In the early phases of habit building, it's a given – we all have to rely on, and work with, our willpower – especially when our willpower reserves are low. As an aside, it's hardly surprising that our reserve of willpower gets drained. According to researchers at Cornell University the average adult faces a whopping 35,000 decisions every day. We make approximately 226 food choices daily alone. Imagine the drain on your willpower when you are trying to avoid the drive-through or working to eliminate wheat or dairy or meat, be pleasant to customers or the boss, and still have enough willpower to go for that run when you get home.

If you can anticipate the times when your willpower reserves are on E then you can pre-plan your responses, push through, and – most importantly – keep your momentum going. On the upside, you will feel better – our brains love that feeling of accomplishment – which, in turn, makes it more likely that you will repeat the process all over again! Here we go...

Listen for your thoughts

Exercise: Anticipate and identify all your unhelpful – low willpower – thoughts: I'm too tired, I've had a long day, I'm hungry, it's too cold, etc.

1.

2.

3.

Identifying your danger zones

Your danger zone is that time of day when your willpower is low and you are likely to talk yourself out of running, walking, or going to the gym.

Exercise: List your top three most crippling, or annoying, low willpower thoughts and when they are most likely to occur. **Personal Example**: I'm too tired to run (low willpower thought), generally happens when I get home from work (danger zone).

My #1 low willpower thought is:

It happens when:

My #2 low willpower thought is:

It happens when:

My #3 low willpower thought is:

It happens when:

Plan for action

Make a plan – a counter response – things you are 100% willing to do (no matter how small) for each low willpower thought and danger zone.

Personal Example: When I get home from work (danger zone). I often think I'm too tired to run (low willpower thought). I will tell myself that it's okay – I can at least run for a few minutes. I will commit to putting my shoes on and going for a ten-minute run (action). After ten minutes I can come home and take a break (planned counter response). **Tip**: Make your action plan super detailed.

Exercise: Create your plan for tackling your top three low willpower situations:

My #1 low willpower thought is:

- My danger zone is:

- Action I will take:

- My planned counter response is:

My #2 low willpower thought is:

- My danger zone is:

- Action I will take:

- My planned counter response is:

My #3 low willpower thought is:

- My danger zone is:

- Action I will take:

- My planned counter response is:

Helpful Hint: Rehearse your plan in your imagination. See every step. All the fine details. Things like having your shoes and socks ready at the door. Eating that snack in the car on the way home, even imagine feeling great after that run.

Reward

I know, after I accomplish my action plan, I will feel... **Personal Example**: stronger, better, more energy, less stressed, accomplished, etc. **Helpful Hint:** This is an important part of the process. The brain likes that feeling of accomplishment when it pushes through something it perceives to be difficult. Each time you push through your low-willpower thoughts, and take action, your brain releases 'feel good' chemicals which makes it more likely that you will repeat the process.

Exercise: Identify three rewards.

1.

2.

3.

Fantastic! You are building your willpower muscle and moving closer to that sustainable habit.

Review and Reflect

(Go to https://katechampionauthor.com/resources/ for your printable Review and Reflect worksheet)

When building any sustainable habit taking some time to review and reflect is an important part of the process. This journey, in many ways, is about self-discovery. Please don't plod along with a plan that is not working for you.

In the early habit-building phases I suggest reviewing and reflecting every four weeks or so. This is your opportunity to think about what's working and what needs adjusting.

Exercise: Set aside some quiet time and take a few moments to consider the following questions:

Measure: How is my current plan working for me?

On a scale of 0 to 10
(0 being it sucks/10 being highly satisfied)

0   1   2   3   4   5   6   7   8   9   10

Reflect: What's going well?

Reflect: What's not going so well?

Ask: How can I improve?

Review: Does my why still fit?

Review: Are my long-term goals still valid?

List: Three things I am most proud/pleased about:

1.

2.

3.

Reflections: Notes about changes/updates I need to make to my plan:

Next review date: _____

Final Words

"A journey of a thousand miles begins with a single step."

– Lao Tzu

THIS CHINESE PROVERB comes from the 6th century BC classic inspirational text – the Tao Te Ching. I love this saying because it reminds me that even the longest, most difficult journey starts with one step.

As I wrote this book, I reflected on my personal running journey – the good, the bad, and the ugly. I started running as a teen as a way to keep myself sane as my life twisted and turned through some rough patches. Up until that point horses were my refuge. I rode, but never ran – unless I was late for something. I seem to remember, after we moved the horse stuff stopped. Somehow – in this new place, new school, new life – I had a flash of inspiration and tried running.

I remember that first run. Frankly, run is an overstatement, however, I do recall that day. I woke up, pulled on a ratty pair of plimsolls (canvas gym shoes), and headed out the door. As I close my eyes I can still see the shade of that cool, quiet, tree-lined lane – and how good it felt to move, get some air into those lungs, and work-up a sweat – that was forty years ago!

Over time, those first steps have evolved into a love for trail running, hiking, backpacking, endurance sports, and a strong value around lifelong health and fitness – for my-self and others.

Whether you are starting out or starting over I hope these words will encourage you to take a small step or two.

Acknowledgements

Heartfelt thanks goes to the running community and everyone who took a moment out of their day to respond to my Facebook posts. A special thank you to the awesome folks at the Back of the Pack Community who are so open-hearted with their support and encouragement.

Through running and writing, my path has crossed with legends like Dan Taylor and Sister Madonna Buder who have been running for the best part of fifty years. I am continually honored by their presence and inspired by their spirit.

Thank you to Helen Baggott for editing, proofreading, and adding sparkle to my words. To the folks at Lighthouse24 for the cover and interior design. And to early readers Kathy Baker, Janet Baughman Cibert, Jamie Beatty, Scott Hagerty, Dan Taylor, and Shirley Warren who have all been so generous with their time and energy. You are greatly appreciated.

Finally, gratitude to close friends and family – you guys rock! I couldn't do this without you!

Need More Support?

Thank you so much for taking the time to read this book. As a writer, mental health professional, runner, and generally curious human the list of things – books, podcasts, blogs, etc. – I personally find useful is continually growing. If you would like more general resources or the specific references for this book please go to https://katechampionauthor.com/resources/ to access my ever-evolving list.

If you enjoyed *Starting Out or Starting Over: Top 10 Tips for Runners* please consider sharing with a friend or leaving a review. You might also enjoy my other books:

Never Too Late: Inspiration, Motivation,
and Sage Advice from 7 Later-in-Life Athletes

And – coming soon:
You Are Limitless

All of which can be found at: https://katechampionauthor.com/

Finally, remember – support, community, and connection with other likeminded people can be found at Back of the Pack Community on Facebook at:
https://www.facebook.com/groups/120829418591397/

Until next time…

Made in the USA
Las Vegas, NV
08 February 2021